the *Secrets* that lie *Within*

the *Secrets* that lie *Within*

*A tale of discovering
the paths to an
optimal life.*

❧

*Discover what
has always been
within your reach.*

Kerry Hearns-Smith & Vicky Arledge

Arbor Publishing
Nashville, Tennessee

Published by Arbor Publishing
7051 Highway 70 South #191
Nashville, TN 37221-2207

Publisher's Cataloging-in-Publication Data
Hearns-Smith, Kerry, and Arledge, Vicky.
        The secrets that lie within / Kerry Hearns-Smith and Vicky Arledge —
Nashville, TN: Arbor Publishing, 2002.

        p.   ;   cm

        ISBN 0-9717967-0-X
        1. Self-actualization (Psychology) 2. Self-realization. 3. Success.
        I. Title

BF637.S4   A75   2002   2002105259
158.1   —dc21   CIP

06 05 04 03 02 • 5 4 3 2 1

Illustrations by Eric Kuhl
Cover illustration by Eric Kuhl

Printed in the United States

Dedication

To Kerry's children, who have been our inspiration throughout this journey. Thank you for being caring, protective, fiercely independent, and adventuresome in real life as well as in our fable. We have truly learned the meaning of "out of the mouths of babes . . . ." We love you!

—Mom and "Aunt" Vicky

Acknowledgments

We could not have accomplished the writing of this book without the passion, professionalism, wisdom, and risk taking of our loving family, friends, and cohorts. We acknowledge and appreciate:

Both of our families who are the "wind in our sails." Without their sheer joy for us, the journey would have been a lot rougher.

Kristi Gilbert, our ever-faithful, logical confidante, and grounding place. Kristi has an amazing gift of taking our concepts and putting them into the words that people can understand and believe.

Jennifer Miller, CEO and owner of SkillSource, has been with us from the beginning — always our alternative ear and our mentor in publishing.

All those who have journeyed with us through our program, Tru•Skills®: An Individual Development Process. Their heartfelt input, their insights, and their growth have been inspirational and validating.

Finally, each other. We have been blessed in sharing our passion for finding our Tru•Self™ and journeying toward our optimal being.

Contents

The Journey Begins!

Cast of Characters

The People of the Village: The hard working people who live day to day to survive and keep up with the heavy demands placed on them by the village ruler. They live in constant fear of falling short of these demands and fear they may fall prey to the TruSlayer dragon.

Sohac and his Clan: The village ruler and his clan. Sohac came to the village and claimed that his own village had been destroyed by the TruSlayer dragon. He offers to lead and protect the village and to help it prosper. With tales of opulence and wonder, he convinces most of the villagers to follow him and his clan.

Arabella: The spirited, flute-playing nymph from the mountaintop. She is caring and wise. She is from the original village, Optimalia, and her spirit comes from the past Optimalians who lived by their values and beliefs and had strong visions and standards by which they led their lives. They lived without judgment and accusations and freely communicated.

Rhianna: Sister of Arabella and mother of McKarin.

Greyson: The kind and tenderhearted son of the village blacksmith and his wife, the village events coordinator. Greyson is a conscientious sole who worries about the needs and well being of those around him. He loves adventure yet approaches it with an abundance of caution and assurance.

Adrie: The adventurous daughter of the village blacksmith and his wife, and younger sister of Greyson. She casts caution to the wind. She is fiercely independent and takes on life zealously. She is caring and loving of all living things.

Finnian: The lighthearted, optimistic son of the village pastor and his wife. He views everything with a sense of humor and is very adventurous. He sees each new day as a new wonder to explore. He is quick to act and views things head on.

Maila: The cautious and controlled daughter of the village correspondent and his wife, the village school teacher. She values thoroughness and self-care. She is always looking to right a wrong.

McKarin: The independent daughter of the village sheriff. Her mother, Rhianna, passed away when she was very young. McKarin prides herself in running her father's home. She is headstrong, enjoys being the leader, and is quick to act.

The TruSlayer Dragon: The demon that Sohac believes to be responsible for destruction. Sohac instills his fear of this demon in the minds of the people within the village.

The Wall of Protection: The stone wall surrounding the village that was built following the storm for the purpose of protecting the village and its people from the TruSlayer dragon.

Chapter 1

The Days of Brightness

It was yet another bright, sunny day. The village was bustling and all the people were moving with a bounce in their step, a song in their hearts, and a hum on their lips. People were sharing, laughing, helping, and taking care of each other. They all seemed to enjoy this life and what they were doing. The village, located near the foot of a beautiful mountain, was very prosperous and its people enjoyed trading with many other nearby villages. This exchange allowed the people to understand, recognize, and learn about the differences in people and their ways. They loved to see new ways of accomplishing daily tasks and loved to see the beauty in what others created.

The community was filled with loving people and strong families. People lived long and happy lives in this abundant village. There were regular celebrations and events that honored and showed gratitude for the wealth of love, community, and traditions that people enjoyed. It was a place of optimal living. In fact, they called it *The Land of Optimalia* because those who lived there had such optimal lives.

On one particular day, a mother and her young daughter were playing in the field amongst the high-flourishing wheat. The sun was warm, and there was a gentle breeze that carried the sounds of laughter across the fields. They were playing a game of hide-and-seek, and the daughter sang as the mother played the flute. The two played for hours in the field until they noticed the sky getting dark. The mother thought it a bit strange since they had come out to the field very early in the day and knew it couldn't have been much past noon.

As they watched the sky darken, the wind began to pick up and a chill was felt in the air. The mother called out to her daughter, "McKarin come, we best tuck the flute away and start heading back to the village."

By the time they returned to the village the wind had become fierce, and there were loud claps of thunder in the distance. People were shocked at how quickly the storm approached and simply stood and watched in amazement. "We have never seen a storm such as this before. What should we do?" was the question several were asking.

The village sheriff came out of his office and suggested, "Go gather your families together and go home to batten hatches and put your livestock in. I will be coming around to your homes to be sure everyone is okay as soon as I am sure my wife and daughter have returned from the fields. I will then be returning to the community center until the storm subsides. I am sure it will pass over quickly, and you will be able to return to your daily business before the day is done. For now, it is best we take precautions."

The sheriff then ran to the edge of the village just in time to see his wife and daughter emerge from the field. Relieved, he said to them, "Let's hurry and get back to the house as quickly as possible."

McKarin held her arms up to her father and he quickly swept her up in his arms. She cried, "Daddy, I'm scared!"

He tried to calm her, "Hush McKarin, everything is going to be just fine. It is probably just a bad storm that will blow over shortly." They rushed to their home, and when they were finally safe inside, he busied McKarin by asking her to go find her dolls. He turned to his wife and said, "You will be safe here. I must go back to check on the others. I told everyone I would stay at the community center." He hugged her and set out for the center.

Within an hour, the wind had become so fierce that it was pulling shingles off roofs of homes and barns. The sky was pitch black, and bolts of lightning were striking in the fields. One of the wheat fields had caught on fire, and the thunder was deafening. The villagers were frightened and anxious.

The storm lasted for hours. The people felt they had no choice but to wait it out and hope and pray that no one would be hurt. They could rebuild what they needed, but they couldn't replace their beloved family and friends. The storm continued to release its rage upon the village throughout the night.

The next morning, as dawn broke, the people began emerging from their homes and their places of refuge. They were shocked to see so much destruction. The community center was essentially gone. Between the wind and the fire caused by the lightning, only the doorway and one wall were still standing. A few of the homes had also caught on fire and only one barn was left standing. Some of the livestock had run off frantically while others had been crushed by the collapsed rooftops.

Over by the remains of the community center, the pastor's wife was yelling, "Help, help, I have found the sheriff. He is caught under a fallen beam. He must have been trying to get out before it collapsed. Help me — I am not strong enough to lift this beam!" Everyone nearby and able rushed to her aid and worked to get the sheriff out. He was alive but badly bruised and battered. He struggled yet finally stood up and slowly thanked the people for pulling him out.

In the days ahead, the villagers were filled with confusion and many unanswered questions as people began cleaning up and salvaging what they could. They had lost six people and many livestock. The village mayor was among those killed, which left people floundering for direction. It was a great loss for the village because he was so respected and admired. He had been the son of the village's founding father, and he had been a remarkable man. He had lived his life guided by his values and taught others how to do so as well. His leadership skills had been an icon of fairness and trust. His family had always come first, though. The sheriff had become a member of that family when he married Rhianna, the mayor's eldest daughter. The mayor even became a mentor to the sheriff. So, in this troubled time, it was only natural that people turned to the sheriff for guidance. Yet they knew the sheriff needed time to recover from his injuries.

The destruction left by the storm was immense. Two fields had been destroyed as well as three main village buildings, and most of the homes needed a great deal of repair. No one had ever seen a storm with such wrath. Their entire world seemed to have changed in an instant from its fury. Even the nearby mountain seemed different with its frequent rumblings and intense glow. There were no answers as to why it had come upon them so unexpectedly. Hence, doubts and fears began to emerge as despair set in. Talk of these fears and doubts began to replace the light-hearted, hopeful discussions of yesterday. The people felt vulnerable and at a loss without leadership and answers as to what really had happened to their beautiful village.

The third day after the storm, a stranger arrived in the village accompanied by six men. He introduced himself, "My name is Sohac, and this is my clan. We have traveled far and need a place to rest ourselves and our horses." Scanning the village and seeing the devastation, Sohac continued, "This is certainly the act of the TruSlayer dragon."

One of the villagers stepped forward and asked, "Are you saying that what happened here was more than a storm? That it was some kind of monster that did this?"

Sohac replied, "Yes, that is exactly what I am saying. I have seen this dragon's destructive path a number of times as we have traveled about. In fact, my own village was destroyed by this terrible dragon, yet we did not fair as well as your village. Most of our people were killed, including both my parents and my only sister." It was clear that he had personally suffered great losses. He went on to tell the villagers tales of the dragon and what he had seen the dragon do. "In fact, I believe your mountain may now be harboring the TruSlayer dragon," he continued. "I would not ignore this demon for you have seen the destruction it can cause. Since we are in need of a place to rest, we would be willing to stay and help you rebuild. We can teach you how to ward off the dragon so it won't strike again. I implore you not to ignore this demon! I would hate to see more devastation come to this village," offered Sohac. The villagers seemed leery of these men yet also felt now was not the time to challenge this stranger who had come unexpectedly and was simply asking for a place to rest. The villagers offered their hospitality from what little they had left.

As the days passed into a week, the villagers began to see Sohac as a leader. They were frightened and needed a sense of security. They didn't have answers for what had happened or why. Day by day, Sohac seemed to put reason to the beliefs and fears that the villagers spoke of. A few felt they could rebuild the village without this out-side intervention and life could be as it was before, yet others needed answers as to why it had happened and why *their* village had been ravaged. They also needed someone to trust. The final decision was made, and a majority of the village agreed to have Sohac stay and follow his guidance and advice.

Sohac quickly took on a governing position by assigning roles and responsibilities to everyone. He firmly believed his approach to be the only way to keep this vil-lage and the people within it safe. During one of his initial village meetings, Sohac explained, "In order to be safe, we must erect a Wall of Protection to keep us in and keep the evil out. We also must be self sustaining and trust and rely on no others." Although people raised questions about Sohac's plans, the questions seemed to be quickly dissipated by more tales of horrible harm and destruction caused by the TruSlayer dragon. Doubts and fears began to overshadow concerns of losing the life they had known. So, the people of the village began to heed his advice and started the process of erecting the wall.

Although most of the villagers were putting their doubts about Sohac and his ways aside, a few of the villagers could not so easily let go of their skepticism. This small group of five villagers merged together after Sohac's initial village meeting and realized they all felt there must be other options to protecting and rebuilding their village. They disagreed with Sohac's advice to totally secure themselves from all that was outside the wall. After all, the village as a whole had been prosperous and had experienced a great deal of success by sharing with other villages and cultures. They recalled the way Sohac quickly dissipated any doubts or questions in the meeting by stating, "Do you dispute the devastation I have seen? Do I need to remind you what can occur when there is no Wall of Protection?" They were beginning to feel that Sohac was overstepping the boundaries of his role as village leader. With Sohac refusing to consider other options for the rebuilding of their village, the few people who were still skeptical began to distrust his motives.

Over the coming days, the five villagers who doubted Sohac tried to communicate their distrust to the other villagers. However, no one wanted to listen to them. It seemed as if the people had allowed their fears to smother their memories of the days of plenitude and happiness. The five decided together that they must take a different approach and search for the truth on their own. They would have to seek out evidence to prove that the fears Sohac was instilling in the villagers were not real.

The village caretaker and his wife; the two daughters of the deceased village mayor, Arabella and Rhianna; and the village historian all agreed to go out and find evidence to disprove Sohac's statements. They were surprised at how quickly so many in the village had given up what they had known to be true for Sohac's beliefs. They knew the people were scared and were hurting from the loss the village had incurred. They also realized that the villagers were looking for any little glimmer of hope to hold on to. The mayor had worked so hard to build a community that supported everyone having their own beliefs. This was the only life his two daughters had ever known. The caretaker and historian had both been very strong advocates of the mayor. In particular, the historian had never heard of the stories that Sohac told. But seeing how quickly the mayor's efforts could be lost, the group was encouraged all the more to discover the truth and seek out evidence that would prove to the rest of the village that they should not be so quick to give up their own beliefs and blindly follow this stranger. After all, his ways were so contradictory to their past ways. They needed to challenge his motives and beliefs. There seemed to be too many stories and conclusions that did not ring true.

The five villagers set up a plan to go and find the proof that would support their distrust of Sohac's motives and invalidate his beliefs. They strongly felt these were simply false beliefs and fears and by providing evidence to discredit them, it would squelch Sohac's fears and also allow the rest of the village to recapture what it had lost. They felt it was their mission to bring back the truth in order to restore the brightness and life back into their village. This was an exceptionally difficult decision for Rhianna. How could she explain to her husband and daughter how important this was to her? How would they ever understand why she needed to leave? After all, she would only be gone a few days, and it was critical for her to play this role and pay testimony to her father's legacy. Her family would have to trust her. This group of five left that evening to find the answers and hoped to return as quickly as possible.

Once outside the Wall of Protection, the small group decided first to visit a few of the nearby villages. As they passed through the nearest field, the historian caught his foot and tripped on something lying on the ground. As he looked down, he realized he had stumbled on the banner bearing the village crest. He shouted ahead to the others, "Look, I have found the crest. It must have been blown out here by the storm." Rhianna ran back to where he stood. She untangled it from the brush and softly spoke, *"The Land of Optimalia."* They all stood in silence for a moment and stared at the symbol the two were holding.

Arabella stated, "This is a sign that we are doing the right thing by going to find the truth. I think we all know that the real truth is more than what Sohac tells or even realizes."

Rhianna folded the crest carefully and handed it to Arabella who offered, "I have room to carry it in my pack. We must be sure it gets back to the village with us."

They stayed close together and helped each other through the rough terrain. They were saddened and disappointed when they found the closest village to them destroyed and deserted. It had been a much smaller village than theirs. The caretaker suggested, "Why don't we camp here tonight, and first thing in the morning we will head toward the next village. The next village is larger and will have more resources. The people who lived here may have gone there in search of refuge."

As dawn broke the following day, the five began their long trek to the next village. When they finally arrived, they found that it also had been ravaged. Yet the atmosphere was very different there. There was activity everywhere. The sounds of hammers pounding and saws cutting could be heard all around. Everyone seemed to be a part of the rebuilding process. As the five slowly walked through the village, they were greeted by a man who appeared to be the village leader. "Welcome to our humble yet somewhat ravaged village. Are you looking for a place of refuge?" he eagerly implored.

"Yes and no," replied Arabella. "We have traveled a long distance to seek answers. Our village was also struck by this unknown force. We have been told it was the work of the TruSlayer dragon."

"Dragon?" questioned the man who had greeted them, "What dragon? I have not heard of such a thing. Please come and rest your weary bodies and we can talk further. It is almost noon, and the village recreation building will be filled with refreshments for all. You see, we are a very supportive community, which is why we have survived this storm and can rebuild."

They all were thankful to be able to sit and rest their tired bodies. The historian began, "Our village was ravaged by a very strange phenomenon and some of our villagers think it was caused by the TruSlayer dragon. It seemed like just a bad storm, yet it came upon us so quickly and caused so much damage. Something also happened to change the nearby mountain as well."

The man replied, "I have never heard of such a dragon as you speak of. We were hit by a devastating storm also. But, that was all it was—just a bad storm. I used to live far from here and storms like this were common. Simply because this was unique to this region does not mean it was created by dragons or demons."

Arabella asked, "If it was simply a bad storm, why did it come upon us so quickly and with so much force? And why has the mountain changed?"

The man sighed, "I realize you all have come a long way and desperately want logical answers that will help you reclaim your lives. I'm sorry. I just don't know those answers. As I said, I have seen storms worse than the one that recently passed through here. Why they occur, I don't know. I certainly don't know why the mountain would have changed. I do know, though, that I don't believe in dragons and demons. Yet they can seem very real when made up in one's mind." He changed his tone and stressed, "We would be more than happy to help with the rebuilding of your village as soon as we get back on our feet, which may take some time as you can see. For now, please stay with us awhile and enjoy our humble hospitality."

"Thank you," replied the caretaker's wife. "You have been very kind and patient. We would appreciate any hospitality you can provide." The five stayed for a week, helped where they could, and questioned the people to learn more and gather evidence to take back with them. They learned a great deal about unusual storms and this village's views on how to rebuild and protect themselves.

It was very different from the view that was now holding their village captive.

At the end of the week, they thanked the neighborly village and bid their farewells. They were anxious to return to their own village. The quickest way back was through the mountain passes. Now that they were quite certain there was no dragon, they agreed to go that route. The mountain passes were difficult. The caretaker had fallen and twisted his leg early in the day's journey and was having a difficult time keeping up. They decided to stop and let him rest for a while. His leg began to swell, and he developed a fever. He had pushed himself as far as he could. His wife finally admitted, "My husband cannot go on any longer. We hate to leave you, yet I now fear for his life. We must seek help."

"I agree with you. He needs more than we can provide," added the historian. It was decided that the village they had left was the closest place for help, so the caretaker and his wife turned back. The historian guided them back a short way to assure they were safe and then returned.

The historian, Arabella, and Rhianna continued on through the mountain passes. The mountain rumbled often which made them uneasy. Midway down the side of the mountain that faced their village they came upon a glowing pit. They stopped beside it, and the historian requested, "I would like to explore for awhile to learn more about why the mountain has changed. I think that if we can find some concrete evidence that makes sense to the people, we can certainly put to rest some of the fears." Rhianna and Arabella agreed and the three set out a plan to explore. They all worked on gathering evidence of any kind that might prove there was no dragon. After several hours, they came back together and sat down to discuss their findings. After much discussion, the historian finally concluded that the mountain had a type of volcanic activity. He explained, "This activity is causing the rumbling, and it may have helped to make the storm more intense. I have read that volcanic activity can cause a great deal of changes in the atmosphere and can even cause changes in weather patterns. It also has been known to create strange phenomenons of energy forces."

With all of the evidence gathered, they were certain Sohac had wrongly steered the people of the village. They had been gone a long time and now felt they had sufficient

evidence to return and show what they had found. They agreed to set out first thing in the morning for home.

As day broke, they set out and made their way down the mountain trails. They stopped to eat and rest often. It was beginning to get dark as they finally reached the base of the mountain. They were elated to see the lights of their village in the distance across the fields, yet a strange site blocked their view of all within. It was a huge stone wall that encircled the entire village. "That must have been what Sohac spoke of as the Wall of Protection," expressed the historian.

"I cannot believe how quickly it was built," replied Arabella.

Rhianna reminded them both, "I think we all felt Sohac's urgency, which is why we left so quickly. He was very serious about getting that wall up as soon as possible. I remember thinking when he spoke at the village meeting that it almost seemed as if he was running from something."

The historian agreed and added, "I had the same feeling. I felt he wanted to shelter the village so much that no outside influence would ever diminish his power or threaten him."

Arabella looked at the historian with surprise and said, "I didn't realize how strongly you felt against him. I don't know that I felt he was so much misusing his power as much as he really believed his tales of the dragon. Let's move on so Rhianna can get to her family and we all can get home in time for bed. I'm exhausted!"

As they started across the field, they were suddenly surrounded by a group of men on horses. One of them shouted, "Stop! You have no business here. This village is protected by the Sohac clan, and no visitors are allowed." The historian quickly stepped in front and stated, "We are not visitors. We are from this village and are simply returning home."

One of the clansmen moved his horse toward the historian to get a better view of his face. He quickly said, "I do not recognize you or the others. Who are you, and why did you leave the village?" The historian introduced them all and stated that they had left shortly after the storm had hit in order to go seek more help and assistance. The clansman rode back to the other men and they conversed for a moment. He then rode back to the three standing in the field and boldly stated, "We have strict orders not to allow anyone unknown into the village. If you had been in the village at the time you say, you would have known that Sohac was the leader and that no additional assistance was needed. You also would not have been able to leave undetected. We cannot allow you to go any further. Please go back to where you have come from, and we will not press this any further."

The historian was enraged at the clansman's explanation. He shouted, "How dare you claim we are not telling the truth! We demand to be taken into the village immediately!" With that, he raised his hand to point toward the village and stepped forward toward the clansman at the same time. The quick motions startled the horse and caused it to rear up. As it came down, the historian was struck in the head by the horse's front hoof. He collapsed instantly. The rider jumped off his horse and tried to revive the historian. He pleaded with the women to leave and that he and his clansmen would help them get back to the base of the mountain, but would do no more for them.

Rhianna stepped forward and pleaded with the clansman, "He was telling the truth! We *are* from the village and want to return to our families. We were only seeking the truth and we have found that there really is no dragon."

The clansman stood, stared at them both, and stated, "If what you say is true, you are calling Sohac a liar."

Arabella quickly added, "No, we know he really believes there is a dragon and fears it so. We only want to help!"

The clansman gathered himself and jumped on his horse. "I suggest you go and tend to your friend. We will tell Sohac what has occurred here tonight, and if he feels it best to allow you into the village, we will be back here at dawn." Arabella and Rhianna felt defeated as they watched the men ride off across the field.

That night, as they made camp at the edge of the mountain, Arabella and Rhianna tended to the historian. His head wound was very deep. By daybreak, they both knew he was not going to wake again. They felt hopeless and angry that they were being kept from their families and at the loss of their friend. Rhianna stood quickly and said, "Our mother and father taught us that the truth shall always prevail. We will find a way to get back to our village and our loved ones with or without the permission of Sohac and his clan. I have a daughter and husband who I know are expecting us. I'm sure they will find us!" Yet, as dawn came and went and there were no clansmen in sight, they became disheartened but were not willing to give up. They would keep trying until they found a way to get back home.

Over the next few weeks more storms came and went. This hindered the women from making much progress. They had searched for shelter and found a cave near the glowing pit. As each day passed and their attempts at entering the village were futile, they sensed a strange energy coming from the glowing pit that gave them strength to keep trying. Remembering what the historian had told them about the creation of energy forces from volcanic activity, they did not question this phenomenon. However, when they were away from the cave for long periods of time, they could feel their energy waning. They were both careful not to stay away for too long.

The day came when Rhianna could stand it no more. She and her sister, Arabella, had made numerous attempts to get past the Wall of Protection, yet to no avail. They had to be cautious so they would not be seen by the Sohac clan since they now knew Sohac did not want them to gain entry into the village. Rhianna decided it was time she try going alone and made a vow that she would not come back until she made it through. She gathered up her supplies and stepped over to where Arabella lay sleeping. She took off her necklace, a precious gift from her mother, and laid it next to Arabella's hand. She then kissed Arabella gently on the cheek and bid her farewell.

Later that night, Arabella awoke from a deep sleep with a start. She felt a painful twist in her heart and looked down to see the necklace lying next to her. She yelled out, "Rhianna!" But knew that Rhianna was not there, nor would she be coming back.

Chapter 2

A Day
in the Village

Twelve Years Later

T welve years had passed since the day that devastating storm had nearly destroyed the village. The
sheriff sat on his front porch and watched the clouds roll by
on yet another overcast day. There hadn't been many sunny
days since that storm. It seemed to have taken the brightness out of the whole world. Things had certainly changed
for the village and its people.

The laughter had been taken over by fear and anxiety. The sense of community and helping each other had been taken over by the need to fend for one's self and one's family. Life had certainly become harder, more demanding, and less giving than the life that many now barely remembered. Most people had resigned themselves to the belief that the days of *old* had passed on forever, almost as if they had never really existed.

The sheriff, in particular, harbored a great deal of hurt and anger for the evil TruSlayer dragon that had destroyed their world, for he had lost his wife, Rhianna, in the days following that storm. Rhianna, along with others, had gone out seeking the truth yet never returned. Sohac's warnings had more truth to them than he had wanted to believe. He feared for the people of the village now because it seemed all that Sohac had believed and feared was true. It had been difficult raising their daughter, McKarin, by himself, yet she had grown into a very wise and responsible person.

As he sat thinking, he couldn't help but feel a pang of sorrow for the village and its people. It was a sad place now. He rose to start his morning walk through the village. As he strolled along, he noted that everything was as it should be. He then followed through with his morning routine of sounding the daybreak bell and opening all the town's buildings. On this day, as he was going through the motions, he thought about each of the villagers and who they had now become.

As the people began rising and going about their routines, the quietness became a rush and disappeared into the daily business. While making his usual rounds, the sheriff stopped to say good morning to the blacksmith. The blacksmith had two wonderful children, Greyson and Adrie, who seemed to give the village back a bit of the light it had lost. His wife, the village events coordinator, tried hard to pull people together and form a community. It just seemed that they were too busy with their own schedule and responsibilities. She worked at her primary duty of keeping the Wall of Protection schedule so that the wall stayed in good condition and the village remained protected. Every adult in the village was assigned weekly responsibilities. Some were assigned sentry duty while others worked to maintain the wall. This immense commitment resulted in a great loss of family time. Yet this seemed to be one of the few remaining activities that brought people together. Having grown up with the blacksmith, the sheriff noticed that the glint of mischief was missing in his friend's eyes and that his wonderful, heartfelt laughter, which the blacksmith had been known for, was no longer heard.

As the sheriff continued on his rounds, he greeted the pastor on his way to the church, "Good morning, Pastor. How is your lovely wife and your son, Finnian?"

"Oh, my wife is busy with decorating the church for the upcoming sermons and hoping more people will come to join us on Sunday morning. We struggle to keep people trusting in their faith and maintaining their health in spirit and mind. But we keep trying. Finnian is keeping himself busy with Adrie most of the time. He really does need to get more serious about finding productive things to do in the village. We don't have that carefree life of long ago anymore, do we?" responded the pastor.

Moving toward the end of the village, the sheriff ran into the village correspondent and his wife, the village school teacher. "Good morning to you both. How are you and your daughter?" asked the sheriff.

"Oh, we are fine, and Maila is doing well. She's studying as much as possible, as always, and of course she and her father love to debate," answered the wife, looking at her husband knowingly. Quickly she added, "I'm running late and need to get to the school. We have so little time to cover just the basics. Oh, how I wish the children could spend more time learning about the ways of life and the world and not just the sad facts of the time." As she left, she waved with a weak smile.

The correspondent mentioned he wanted to learn more about the neighboring villages.

"You know that Sohac does not agree with that idea and pursuing it may endanger you," warned the sheriff.

"Don't you ever wonder, Sheriff?" argued the correspondent. "We knew another time and way of life."

The sheriff calmly answered, "Yes, but that is gone. What good does it do to open the wounds? Keep to your normal reporting—it's what the people know and expect."

As the sheriff walked back to his office, it struck him how much he simply went through his motions each day. His life supporting Sohac and playing out his orders had become a mindless routine. The village simply operated on automatic everyday. The people did their duties and then went home to their families to eat, maybe talk a bit, and go to bed—only to then start the same routine again the next day. People seemed tired most of the time, and arguments were an everyday occurrence. The sheriff spent much of his time dissipating these arguments and trying to keep people on track. The village never seemed to prosper because any revenue not needed to sustain minimum daily needs was given to Sohac to pay for maintaining the Wall of Protection and keeping the village safe and protected. Maybe that was part of why no one seemed very happy. There wasn't an abundance of anything anymore. Sohac saw this as being a successful and self-sustaining village. However, it was becoming clear to the sheriff that although Sohac had won his leadership position with talk of prospering and abundance for the entire village, Sohac was the only one reaping the rewards.

The sheriff stopped and shook himself out of his melancholy mood. "I have work to be done. Our life is good. We are safe, and we still have our village that is self-sustaining. We should be happy with that!" he reminded himself.

Chapter 3

The Adventure

Several of the children in the village were very close to each other. They seemed to stand out due to their zest for life, their constant scheming, their many adventures, and close family ties. Most of these children were excused from the basic day-to-day chores because they tended to create more work than help when they got involved. Finnian and Adrie were typically the two to get things started. As usual, they were off to explore once again. It was a typical adventure for them. Yet on this day they decided to go to the mountain edge where they had been told repeatedly not to go. It was believed that the TruSlayer dragon lived within the mountain. If their parents knew they were *this* far outside the Wall of Protection, they would surely be in trouble. But despite this fact, off they went! The ever-present glowing light and rumbling coming from the mountain seemed just too enthralling to be left unexplored.

As they drew closer to the mountain, they heard a sound that they had heard before, yet it seemed clearer today. It drew them nearer. It was unmistakably a flute—a very lilting sound. Their curiosity got the best of them. With one glance back at the village, they decided to climb part-way up the mountain to determine the source of the music. They climbed for nearly an hour and found that the mountain rock was much harder to climb than they had thought it would be. They saw a ledge just above them and what seemed to be a pass. They looked at one another and nodded their heads, silently agreeing they would rest on the ledge. As they continued to climb, Finnian turned and grabbed Adrie's hand to give her a lift.

They both took a deep breath, and with a mixture of fear and curiosity, they crept along the rock wall through the pass. As they rounded the corner, they saw a glow. "It must be a fire someone has built," whispered

Finnian. As they cautiously moved closer, the flute playing started again. They could see a shadow of someone on the rock wall in front of them, but they were hesitant to move closer for fear of making a noise and being discovered. So, they sat down and listened to the beautiful flute music and watched the shadow gracefully move back and forth in front of the fire. They had sat there for some time when the shadow disappeared and the flute playing stopped. They looked at one another but dared not move without knowing where the person had gone. Just when Finnian was about to motion to Adrie, a face popped out from behind the rock wall they were leaning against. It startled everyone. Adrie jumped up to run. Finnian took a stance and prepared to defend himself and Adrie.

The shadowy figure slipped from the start the children gave her. As she regained her footing, she softly pleaded, "Please don't fear me." Finnian cautiously let his guard down a bit as Adrie stopped in her tracks and slowly crept back to his side.

They both stood and stared for a moment amazed at what they saw. Before them stood a beautiful, tiny woman

who almost seemed like she was floating and more spirit-like than human. They both said in unison, "Who are you?"

"I am Arabella, and please know that I mean you no harm. I'm so excited to have visitors. It's very lonely up here. Come with me over to the fire," she implored.

They slowly and cautiously followed Arabella around the large rock wall that had blocked their view earlier. They came upon a huge split in the mountain rock with a pit that glowed brightly. With some amazement, Finnian expressed, "This must be the light that can be seen from the village."

Arabella motioned and said, "Come, sit by the fire." It was warm and inviting. She explained, "I live here on the mountain and am so happy to have company to share with." She wanted to know all about these two curious children and how they came to be on the mountain. The children introduced themselves and told Arabella who they were, leaving out very little. For some reason both children trusted Arabella instantly and wanted to know more about her as well. They told her that they had been told not to come to the mountain because of the TruSlayer dragon and that the dragon had supposedly destroyed their village and others as well.

Finnian asked Arabella, "Have you seen the TruSlayer dragon, and aren't you afraid of it?"

Arabella replied, "I have yet to meet this dragon you speak of." Just then, a rumble started deep inside the mountain and seemed to bubble up through the huge fire pit in front of them. Finnian and Adrie fidgeted nervously. Arabella explained that the rumbling was a normal occurrence and it was simply the mountain speaking and settling and that there was nothing to fear from it. "In fact," continued Arabella, "it is this energy from the mountain that keeps me alive. You see, I am more spirit than physical being now."

Adrie and Finnian weren't quite sure what to make of all Arabella was saying to them. "She seems real though," thought Adrie.

"She certainly looks real," thought Finnian.

Arabella continued and said, "I have lived on this mountain for many, many years now. I was one of the fortunate ones I suppose. My sister and I had discovered this area of the mountain and its energy that sustained us. Yet my sister still felt drawn to return to her family and chose to leave for too long. She never made it back to her family nor to the mountain. I have grieved the loss of her ever since."

Arabella then asked Finnian and Adrie if they would like to hear her tell them some legends and tales. They both loved stories and they were reluctant to leave, so they said, "Oh, yes! We would love to hear them!" Arabella told them about people and a village that existed long ago. It was a very bright and happy place full of adventure and hope. Finnian and Adrie loved the stories, but it was starting to get dark and they knew they must be getting back to the village. They reluctantly told Arabella, "We must go but may we come back, and would you tell us more stories?" She happily agreed. As they were leaving, Adrie turned and asked Arabella, "Would you mind if we brought others with us to hear your stories?"

Arabella was pleased that Adrie asked and she said, "I would be honored, but please only bring those who you know can be trusted to keep this place and the stories a secret."

Adrie agreed, and as they made their way back to the village, Adrie asked Finnian, "Why do you think Arabella lives on the mountain all alone and why does she not want anyone to know about her?"

"I guess we will have to ask her the next time we see her," replied Finnian.

"I can't wait to tell Maila and Greyson about this," Adrie chimed in.

"What about McKarin?" asked Finnian.

"I don't know. Do you think she would scold us for going to the mountain?" asked Adrie. On the way back to the village, the two pondered what Arabella had told them. There were a lot of similarities in her stories to those that they had heard from Adrie's mother and Finnian's father of a time when their village was a happy and bright place.

The next two days were stormy, and the children were getting impatient with waiting to go back to see Arabella. Finally, the storm broke, and the children planned their trek to the mountain. This time, they took Maila and Greyson with them. Greyson was anxious and said, "We probably shouldn't be going up the mountain. What if someone catches us?"

Adrie replied, "No one comes out this far because they fear the dragon."

Maila wondered aloud, "Shouldn't *we* fear the dragon?"

Finnian responded, "I'm having some doubts about whether or not there really is a dragon."

They trekked up the mountain and found Arabella right where they had left her on their previous trip. They introduced Maila and Greyson, and they all sat down around the fire and listened for hours to more of Arabella's stories. They were stories that told of people following their hearts and living without fears. There were tales of people enjoying each other and every moment of their lives. The characters in her stories all were prosperous and successful people who celebrated often and lived joyously, who cared for each other and worked for the betterment of their community, and who shared their likenesses and respected their differences. No *one* set of beliefs was followed—rather a mixture and wealth of beliefs for a common good. These stories and their characters left the children feeling excited and wanting to hear more. They also sang songs. One in particular seemed to enthrall the children.

There are many out there who will make you doubt.
There are many out there who judge you.
They have lost their way and cannot hear their heart.

Listen to your heart, can you hear it?
Believe in your heart, will you trust it?
Follow your heart, do you know it?

There are those who tell no truth.
There are those who have no faith.
They have lost their message and cannot trust their heart.

There are many who will misguide you.
There are many who see only their way.
They have lost their hope and do not know their heart.

Listen to your heart, can you hear it?
Believe in your heart, will you trust it?
Follow your heart, do you know it?

Wonders of light will guide you through the night and into
the daylight. Trust in your hopes and dreams, follow your
passions. Let this inspire you to find your true life.

When you finally believe and listen, you will discover your
true self. Know who you are and never let it go.

They sang it over and over. Adrie asked Arabella, "Where did this song come from?"

Arabella responded, "It was created by two people who watched their homes and their loved ones be taken away. It is a reminder to us all that we must find the messages inside ourselves—for we have always known them—and allow them to be our true guide."

The children decided it was time to go and sadly said goodbye to Arabella. As they made their way back to the village, they couldn't stop humming the song and talking about how interesting the stories were that Arabella told. "Do you really think they are true?" asked Finnian.

"I know they are," said Adrie.

Greyson added, "It would be nice if they are, but I'm not sure."

Maila replied, "Even if they are, nothing like that could happen in our world."

Maila asked, "Adrie and Finnian, why did you not ask McKarin to go to the mountain?" They looked at each other and both replied that they thought she would not want them to go back and that she would tell on them. Maila said, "McKarin may better understand Arabella's stories because she is the oldest and knows stories of when things were different. I will talk with her and see if she would like to go back with us."

That night as Maila prepared for bed, she started her nightly journaling with questions. "What do Arabella's stories mean? Who is she? Why have they just now discovered her?" She continued to journal and found herself jotting thoughts from Arabella's stories.

MAILA'S THOUGHTS:

- Follow and Believe in your heart; this will keep fears away.
- Enjoy life and celebrate.
- Care for one another and help create the community.
- Respect differences and share your beliefs.
- There is no one right way for all.
- Find the messages inside yourself.

As she reflected over what she had written, Maila silently thanked her father, the village correspondent, for his constant encouragement to journal, which helped her clearly focus her thoughts.

The next day, Adrie and Finnian were bored while they waited to hear back from Maila. Finnian decided he had better help his father repair the door on the church right away so that he could go to the mountain later. Adrie wandered off in search of something to do or someone to talk to. As she strolled by the gate to Sohac's manor, Adrie noticed an array of bright colors up near the manor's entrance. She quietly maneuvered around the gate and made her way up to the front of the manor. There she found a garden of bright flowers. She couldn't resist picking some of the daisies. As she was admiring the flowers and humming, she heard a gruff voice behind her. She turned to see a tall man with his hands on his hips glaring at her. She let out a soft giggle and wrinkled her nose. "I guess you caught me," she admitted.

He, in no uncertain terms, demanded, "Who are you? How dare you trespass and pick my flowers!" To his chagrin, she turned and proceeded to pick another handful of daisies. He reached out and grabbed her arm. She swung around, and, with a huge smile and mischief in her big blue eyes, presented him with the bouquet of flowers. He stammered for a moment and then composed himself. He let go of her arm and reluctantly accepted the bouquet. "Thank you," Sohac said gruffly.

"I like pretty things and flowers are just so bright and carefree," Adrie explained. "You are so lucky to have such a beautiful garden. It is really the only bright spot in the village. I'm Adrie, can I come here often, please sir?" she boldly continued.

He was at a loss. This little sprite of a girl was not afraid of him nor was she afraid to ask for what she wanted. He admired that. In a no-nonsense voice, he replied, "You may come here, as you wish, but the flowers must stay here, and you are not to bring anyone else."

"Oh, thank you sir!" she blurted out, and before he realized what she was doing, she flung herself at him and gave him a big hug. Then as quickly as she came, she was skipping off toward the gate. "Goodbye, kind sir. I'll see you tomorrow." Her voice trailed off as she skipped away. Sohac stood there dumbfounded and then turned to go back into the manor. Glancing down at the bouquet, he shook his head and wondered if he had imagined what had just happened. It had seemed almost magical.

Two days later the children set out again for the mountain, this time with McKarin. They talked all the way and told McKarin of the wonderful stories Arabella had recounted and the happiness of the characters. It seemed that the stories all had a life of their own, and the children longed to be a part of that. The stories depicted such a happy, carefree, and secure life. McKarin wondered who this person was who lived all by herself up in the mountain. She was intrigued, yet somewhat skeptical, and was anxious to meet her.

They finally made it to the pass in the mountain, and Arabella was there playing her flute. Adrie danced up to her and gave her a big hug. Finnian began singing their song and twirled Maila around. McKarin looked at Finnian strangely as he sang. Greyson introduced McKarin to Arabella. Arabella gazed at McKarin as if she had seen a ghost and then quickly collected herself and welcomed her.

She asked the children, "What have you been up to since you left?"

They replied, "Oh, we have talked a lot about the stories you told us. We have questions about how the people stayed so happy and knew how to live the way they did."

Arabella explained, "When people live by what is in their hearts and reserve judgment of each other, it is amazing how peaceful, prosperous, and loving life can be. It is not difficult to live in harmony when everyone understands that they are connected by a common thread and must keep themselves healthy in order to be at their potential. The hardest part is trusting yourself instead of the false beliefs and fears that will misguide you and hold you back. As long as you are held back, it is very difficult to reach your optimal being or potential."

Finnian interrupted, "Optimal what . . .? What does that mean, Arabella?"

Arabella laughed at his frustration and continued, "Unless you see yourself with clarity and trust yourself, you will develop false beliefs. Those false beliefs and fears hinder you from moving toward happiness and your optimal being. Optimal being is the place you come to when you are only guided by your heart and your true beliefs—it is your Tru•Self."

"Wow, that seems like it would take a lifetime, and then some, to accomplish," Finnian replied.

Adrie chimed in, "Oh, I don't know. It isn't that hard to listen to your heart. Mine speaks very loudly most of the time."

"Adrie, you have a special gift for listening. Yet, you are also right Finnian, there are different paths to get to optimal being. For most people, it *is* a life-long journey. Too often though, people spend more of their lives working from false beliefs and ignore their real needs and what is in their hearts rather than actively working on finding and knowing their Tru•Self," Arabella concluded.

Finnian asked, "Will you teach us how to do that?"

Arabella smiled at him and said, "I was hoping you would ask that." Arabella then told them a story of a young girl and how she loved to play in the fields, pick flowers, and weave flower crowns. The little girl used to say that everyone deserved to be a princess and must be crowned.

Before Arabella was able to finish her story, McKarin abruptly stood up and said, "We must go right now!"

The children all said, "But Arabella is not done yet."

McKarin said, "Fine! You stay and get in trouble. I'm not going to!" The children watched as she hurried off. They told Arabella a bit about McKarin. They told her that McKarin was the oldest of them all and that the TruSlayer dragon had killed her mother. That was part of the reason she was very leery about coming to the mountain.

"Something must have frightened her," said Adrie. They decided they didn't want her to have to go back alone so they also should leave.

Before they left, Arabella mentioned, "McKarin may not know all she needs to know. I wish you well until we meet again."

The children caught up to McKarin, and Maila asked her, "What is wrong? Why did you leave so abruptly?"

McKarin said, "Arabella seems like a nice person, but who is she? Why does she have all these stories? I don't think we should go back there."

As Maila journaled that night, she contemplated the sense she had that McKarin had been very frightened and upset that afternoon. She poured over the story Arabella had been telling in hopes of finding a clue. Her thoughts kept going back to Arabella's comment of how the young girl in the story had said, "Everyone deserves to be a princess and to be crowned." Maybe that had upset McKarin. Maila thought that idea through and realized that some of her happiest and most carefree times had been when she and McKarin used to sneak into McKarin's father's room and put on the many hand-made crowns from McKarin's mother's trunk. Her mother had made crowns out of almost anything imaginable. Then Maila remembered the day McKarin's father had found them playing in the room and scolded them. That was the last time they had played *princess*. "Of course!" thought Maila. Arabella's story had brought back sad memories of McKarin's mother. Maila thought through the dialog of the story and tried to capture the message she thought Arabella was trying to tell.

 MAILA'S THOUGHTS

- Listen to your heart and really hear it.
- See others without judgment.
- Stay healthy in spirit, mind, and body.
- We are all connected by a common thread.
- Trust in your heart and yourself instead of false beliefs and fears.
- Optimal being is finding and reaching your true self.
- There are many different paths to do this.
- It is a life-long journey.

"Maybe I'll share this with McKarin. It might help her," thought Maila.

The children all decided to heed McKarin's advice, at least for a few days. They didn't want to get into trouble, and they really couldn't answer McKarin's questions of who Arabella really was.

McKarin had gone straight home that afternoon and started making dinner for her father. She told him she wasn't feeling well and went to bed early. She wasn't sure what it was about Arabella or the stories she told that unsettled her, but something was too familiar and frightening. She pondered, "Was it the song that Finnian had sung? The tune seemed so familiar. Was it the story of the young girl? It sounded like her mother and her as a child."

The following day the children decided they would stay close to home and met to decide if they would go back to see Arabella or not. Adrie, Finnian, Maila, and Greyson talked at length and tried to understand why her stories were so intriguing and what they really meant. Why were they so drawn to see Arabella again? Maila, being the levelheaded one, tried to bring logic into the tales by sharing her journaled thoughts with them. They all decided that they liked and trusted Arabella and felt she was trying to tell them something important. So they decided that they would go back at least one more time to see Arabella. They needed to understand *why* Arabella was trying to teach them something. They knew that this trip might be longer than the others, so they all packed provisions for a long day of adventuring.

Greyson and Maila talked the whole way about what may be the true meaning in the stories. Finnian and Adrie laughed at how deep in thought and conversation Greyson and Maila became and teased, "You both are taking this far too seriously. Let's just have fun."

They found Arabella and again sat and listened to more tales. Before they left though, Arabella asked them to follow her. "You must work together to be able to reach the point where I will be taking you," she guided. She led them along a treacherous and narrow path that steeply inclined toward the top of the mountain. It was a tough and scary climb. They all worked together and by using all of their strengths, they finally neared the peak. As they rounded a corner, there before them was a beautiful sunset. The orange, red, and yellow hues were breathtaking. Never before had the children remembered seeing such a wondrous sight. Arabella explained, "This is where the aura of the mountain comes from and it is like this all of the time. It is as your village used to be." The children all sat and stared for awhile and took in the warmth and beauty.

Greyson finally said, "This is why you have told us all the stories. You believe we can help to change our village."

She smiled at Greyson and said, "Yes, I do believe that, but you must remember that people will only believe what they see with their own eyes. It has taken each of you time to begin to see the value of these messages. As you have learned here, unless we all work together to satisfy needs, it can be very difficult. Remember that your Tru•Self cannot be found without your needs being met. When your needs are continually met, because you have asked for and found healthy means to meet them, there is no need for fear—only happiness and peace. You must show the people around you how this can happen. By confronting your own fears, you can show the people how to change and satisfy their own needs." Arabella then told them, "This quest toward change and toward an optimal life takes time. You should not come to see me for a while. You need to figure out what the stories mean and you can only do that on your own." She then revealed, "You see, I am very much like you and have lived these tales and stories I have told. They *can* be lived by you." She stepped over to Adrie and holding her hand she said, "Adrie, you keep the spirit alive within the village. Remember to always act from your heart." She moved to Finnian and expressed, "Finnian, you are the laughter. You see the brightness in all. Keep that light burning." She took Greyson's hand and said, " Greyson, you are the conscience of the village. You bring the assurance and knowing that all is okay. Stay faithful to all you know and love. And, finally, Maila you are the logic and determination for all to overcome fears. Help people see this. You all are the voices of the village. The people of the village do not see or hear it yet, but you all can bring these gifts to them and yourselves. They are the gifts of true beliefs and life without fear. There is no TruSlayer dragon. It is only fear that keeps this dragon alive. Go and determine for yourselves what this all means. I will be here for you, but you must discover this on your own."

The children left with many questions on their minds. If there was no TruSlayer dragon, what was there to fear? What then had caused the changes in the village?

What had really happened to McKarin's mother? They certainly had a lot of discoveries to make.

Maila excused herself early that night. She was so anxious to journal all that had transpired that day. She started by thinking through Arabella's stories. There were so many.

 MAILA'S THOUGHTS:

- Your needs must be met in order to find your true self and reach your optimal being.
- We must ask to get our needs met.
- Confronting your fears and recognizing your false beliefs helps you to move forward toward optimal being.
- Help others to recognize fears and false beliefs and meet their needs.
- We must see with our own eyes in order to believe.
- Only you can do this for yourself.
- Be patient, this takes time.
- Remember to always act from your heart.

Chapter 4
The Secrets Unfold

The children all met the following day and discussed everything that had happened during their visit with Arabella the day before. They knew they would have to find creative ways to help people see and understand the lessons Arabella had taught them. Maila suggested, "I think the people of the village need to see these lessons put into action by those closest to them. This may be the only way for people to actually believe the outcomes that are possible."

Greyson voiced, "If there was no TruSlayer dragon—if this was made up from false beliefs—then what was there to fear? These fears must be coming from within." The children decided they must overcome their own false beliefs and fears to set an example. So each one of the children chose from within themselves their own false beliefs and fears to confront and work to dispel or change. These were not easy to uncover, yet Arabella had helped each of the children to see within more clearly and to recognize these fears. The foursome promised to help each other to do this. Adrie chose her fears of being controlled and losing freedom. Greyson chose his fear of trying the unknown and his false belief of being rejected. Finnian chose his fear of being hurt and false belief of not matching up to expectations. And Maila chose her fear of not doing the "right" thing. They made a vow to each other that they would work on these false beliefs and fears by using the lessons Arabella had been teaching them. This would show the people the power of the lessons. If they could overcome their own false beliefs and fears, maybe this would show their loved ones how false beliefs can lead to fears that stop people from moving forward and working toward their optimal being.

Greyson went off to see what his father was doing. He had always been somewhat afraid of the horses his father shoed, especially the ones that were trapped in the barn because he knew they could start at any moment and go wild. He also felt that he wasn't matching up to his father's wishes because he tended to not try things if he feared them. This left him feeling rejected because his father never asked him to help. He found his father and sat on the workbench for a while and watched him. Greyson suddenly asked his father if he would show him how to shoe a horse.

"I thought you didn't want to ever do this because it was so dangerous," stated his father.

"I'd like to learn from you," said Greyson. So, although anxious, Greyson watched intently and then slowly took the horse's hoof. The horse pranced a bit, which startled Greyson. He backed up and decided to watch a bit longer.

The next day, he awoke with his father and resolved to himself that today he would actually do the shoeing on his own. He went to the shop with his father. His father mentioned, "The pastor's horse needs shoeing and he is a docile animal. Why don't you start with him?"

"Thank you, Father. I appreciate the assurance. I guess I need that more than I thought," Greyson admitted. Greyson started humming to himself and found he was able to calm himself and the horse and was then able to shoe the horse. His father congratulated him and thanked him for wanting to learn his trade. "I would like to help you out from now on, Father," Greyson said. His father smiled and said, "I'd welcome the help." With that, Greyson left to go finish his chores. His father sat in amazement over the changes in his son's behavior and couldn't help but feel a sense of pride in his son's willingness to confront his own fears.

Finnian searched for a way to address his fear of being hurt and noticed that every time his father had asked him to help, it was with menial tasks only and things that would not require Finnian to really take responsibility. That Sunday, Finnian asked his father, "Might I be able to deliver the children's sermon?"

At first his father said, "No, one must be prepared for such a sermon and be willing to be a good role model. The children are very impressionable." Finnian told his father he had prepared a sermon and that he needed to be trusted so he could prove he could do this well. His father contemplated a moment. "Finnian, if you are serious about this, you must prove to me you can do this before I put the children in your hands. Prepare a sermon on the importance of responsibilities and deliver it to me this week. If I feel you are on the right track, you may deliver it next Sunday." Finnian agreed and went to get started on this new project with a great deal of enthusiasm.

Adrie went off to see Sohac and spend some time in the gardens. She decided to collect a bouquet with as many varieties as possible. As she wandered through the gardens, she noticed a group of beautiful water lilies down by the stream. "They would brighten up the fountain in the courtyard," she thought. She realized she had been warned several times about the dangers of the stream by her parents and Sohac himself, yet she was drawn toward the stream. Determined she was going to get those lilies, she made her way to the edge. As she stepped on one of the old boards that edged the stream, the board snapped and she fell in. Sohac, who had been watching from inside the manor, saw her and rushed out to help her. As he approached, he realized that Adrie had hit her head and was not moving. He ran down to her and swept her out of the river. His heart was pounding. As he cradled her in his arms, he patted her cheek to try to revive her. He caught his breath as she slowly opened her eyes and smiled. He quickly scolded her, "I warned you against going near the stream."

In that instant, she saw the worry in this gruff man's eyes and realized how her free spirit really did cause others to worry. She softly apologized, "I swear I won't do it again.

Thank you for saving me!" He set her down and straightened his clothes with a nervous twitch. He was surprised at how fierce his reaction was when he thought she might really be hurt. She explained she was trying to get him some water lilies for his fountain in the courtyard. "May I put them in your fountain, Sohac?" she asked. He slowly smiled and gave his permission. As Adrie walked over toward the fountain, she began to realize that her fear of being controlled often drove her to careless acts which only created fear and worry in those who cared for her. This was a profound realization because her actions were actually forcing people to worry about her instead of approve of her and give her freedom. She vowed that she would start to be more aware of what effect her actions had on others. After putting the flowers in the fountain, she turned and addressed Sohac, "Sohac, I really am sorry for being so careless. I will be more aware and cautious from now on."

Maila had always thoroughly contemplated her moves. As she sat and gathered her thoughts, she chose to heed what was in her heart and not worry about how it was going to come across. Then she pulled out her journal and reviewed what she had written of her experiences with Arabella. She began by writing a letter to McKarin that told of her personal thoughts and beliefs about Arabella's stories. She explained that she was seeking help from McKarin, even though it may be very hard for McKarin to face.

My Dearest McKarin,

It is with much love for you, my best friend, that I share these thoughts. You know that we have all been on an extraordinary journey recently. We have met and spent time with an amazing person who has shared thought-provoking stories.

I know so much of what has occurred has frightened you and brought back difficult memories for you to deal with. I also realize there is still so much unanswered. You know me well, McKarin. You know I must always research until I am comfortable with the information and what I believe. But I am finding I trust my heart. You may call this faith, as that is the act of stepping out and trusting that which cannot be seen or proven. I am finding that faith in Arabella and her stories.

I would like to share my journaled thoughts. Some of the lessons we have learned:

- *Sometimes lessons come from unexpected, almost magical, sources.*
- *Distrust is something we have been taught. This distrust is deep seeded and has created our fears.*
- *When we are afraid, we have to blame everything that is wrong on someone or something else.*
- *If we live in fear, then we build walls around us and our needs go unmet.*
- *We must take care of ourselves so that we can have the energy to live a fulfilled life.*
- *Beware of people who have all the answers. They may lead us astray.*
- *Our life can be better when everyone respects each other and cooperates to create a better good.*
- *When we follow and listen to our hearts, we can trust that our journey will be successful and we will find our true self and reach our optimal being.*

I hope you will be open to what I am sharing with you. Your dearest friends have been working hard to become living examples of how things can change. . .

Maila went on to further explain the many lessons Arabella had been teaching and how Adrie, Greyson,

Finnian, and she vowed to find ways to put these lessons into action by confronting their own false beliefs and fears and proving things could change. Maila wrote that she was seeking help from McKarin even though it may be very hard for her friend to face. It just was not right that the village had no light or spark anymore and that the people seemed to have very little sense of purpose, belonging, or passion. She also explained that she truly believed there was no TruSlayer dragon and, if that was the case, then this dragon could not have killed McKarin's mother. The letter turned into a journaling of what was in Maila's heart. She told McKarin that she realized that she did not have all the answers, but knew things needed to change.

As she was finishing the letter, her father came in and asked what she was doing. Maila looked at the letter and back at her father. She had always confided in her father and respected his views. She felt a strong need to share this with her father. She had known for a long time that her father was warring with things he wanted to talk and write about to others. So she looked at him, handed him the letter, and simply asked him, "Please, Father, I ask you to keep it between us for now." He took the letter and sat down to read it.

After reading the letter, her father looked up and said, "Maila, you have become an exceptional writer with a gift of speaking from your heart — it becomes you. I think McKarin needs to see this letter and the village needs to hear the concepts. Will you take the essence of this and help me write an editorial for the village newsletter?"

Maila was surprised and relieved at her father's reaction. She agreed, but also said, "Father, won't this cause problems?" Her father looked at her and said, "Maila, you have shown the courage to write this for a friend. I need to have that kind of courage, also."

She put the letter in an envelope and walked over to McKarin's house. McKarin was sitting on the front porch. Maila handed her the letter and asked that she wait until she was alone that night to read it. McKarin looked at her puzzled yet accepted it and agreed. McKarin could sense a change in Maila. Something seemed different. She seemed nervous but also anxious in a positive way. So, she asked Maila if she wanted something to drink, and the two sat and chatted for a while.

Late that night, as McKarin crawled into bed, she noticed the letter on her nightstand. She propped her pillow up, opened the envelope, and unfolded the letter inside. She began reading. First she was curious, then puzzled, then hurt, then angry, and finally anxious to learn more and talk more about all of this. The letter brought up so many questions, but also gave her some answers. They were answers she had for some time ignored yet longed for. She now realized that it was her fear of hearing something she didn't want to about her mother that held her back from knowing the truth.

McKarin decided she needed to go see Arabella to seek answers to her questions. She thought, "I will ask Maila to go with me and show me the way." She shut off her light but found she could not sleep. At dawn she went to find Maila. The two set out to find Arabella. Arabella was surprised to see the two girls yet sensed McKarin was the reason they were there. Arabella welcomed them and asked the girls to sit and tell her what she could do for them. Maila sat silently through the conversation. McKarin had many questions, and Arabella was very willing to answer them. Maila couldn't help notice that Arabella seemed to be very cautious with what she told McKarin, almost as if she were holding something back. They must have been there over two hours when McKarin finally said she needed to get back before her father missed her. She thanked Arabella and asked if she could return. "Certainly," Arabella replied.

The two girls hurried back to the village in a strange silence. That night, McKarin found herself feeling overwhelmed but still curious to know more. She decided to go back to see Arabella the next morning by herself.

The next day McKarin went back to the mountain and searched for Arabella. She was surprised not to find her where she had been the times before. She called out for her, but no one answered. She decided to sit and wait with the hope that she would soon return. As she sat, she realized how tired she was. She hadn't slept well for two nights due to all the thoughts and questions going around in her mind. She decided to lie back against the rock behind her and rest her eyes. She awoke with a start! She jumped up and looked around. The sun was starting to set and she realized she had slept for hours. She called out to Arabella once more and decided to go back to the village. As she trekked back, she began to contemplate her dream. It had been a strange dream about her mother and her in a field and a storm. Then it turned to two young women, her mother and another, climbing a mountain. The young women were beautiful and full of life. Then she remembered something about them trying to break through a wall and being chased away. The two women went back to the mountain and seemed to change from human to spirit forms. One was restless and sad and tried to again get past the wall, but her energy drained and she couldn't get through. She was struggling to reach the mountain and she softly said, "I love you, McKarin. Goodbye, Arabella." Her dream was very confusing and unsettling. She turned her attention to getting home as quickly as possible. She would talk to Maila about the dream and see if any of it made sense to her.

Chapter 5

Living the Lessons

T wo days later, McKarin was surprised to see in the village newsletter an article written by Maila's father that sounded very similar to the letter Maila had written to her. McKarin recalled the turmoil the letter had created within her and the questions it raised in her mind. She had always thought of herself as a fairly open person, and even though she understood it all a bit better now, the letter and the dream made her want to know more. At the same time though, she felt as if she didn't want to let go of what she knew life to be like now. She couldn't help but wonder that if *she* reacted this way, others who read this article would be even more confused and possibly more upset than she. She was amazed and concerned that Maila's father had gone so far out on a limb. His newsletters had always been conservative and practical. This certainly wasn't the kind of article he had ever written or printed before. McKarin also felt a bit betrayed by seeing such similar thoughts as to what had been in Maila's letter. McKarin put the newsletter on the dining room table where her father always looked for it and headed to go see Maila.

By the following morning, there was a tense feeling in the air throughout the village. The article created many discussions. There was a lot of confusion over where these thoughts and concepts were coming from. Many were questioning, "Why would the correspondent write something like this, and why now?" Others tried to reason why the thoughts made a good deal of sense. There were fears that this would misguide the children or deter people from the importance of keeping the village safe from the TruSlayer dragon. There were also subtle and less-talked-about feelings such as the yearning to know more and to possibly believe in a different way of life. Many people had questions they wanted answered, but most knew that if they openly pursued answers to those questions, they could end up with repercussions they weren't ready to deal with. Most felt it best to wait and see how Sohac would react to the article.

Sohac was still livid the following morning but had cooled enough to confront the correspondent. When he read the article he had been shocked and couldn't believe the correspondent would be so irresponsible as to put false hopes and fairy tales in people's minds. "It also could have the potential to destroy the village and all I have tried to do for these people," thought Sohac.

He immediately set out to find the correspondent. He found him in his office and barged right in. As he came through the door, the correspondent quickly stood up and held out his hand, "I know you must be angry with me, but before you say anything, will you please give me a chance to explain?"

"Angry is mild for what I am feeling, but I will hear you out," replied Sohac.

The correspondent explained that he felt strongly about his beliefs and that he believed it was only right to enlighten people in as many ways as possible. He was very careful not to mention that Maila had been the one to introduce him to the concepts because he did not want her to receive any of Sohac's wrath. But he felt comfortable believing these thoughts and ideas. As he had read Maila's letter, there was something about the messages that seemed so right and true to him. The thoughts plagued his mind and he spoke to Sohac, "It only makes sense that people should help one another and yet take good care of themselves. Only through this care may they really find their Tru•Self. Also, it seems to be common sense that people should be able to be unique and yet respect each other's differences. Finally, knowing and understanding what is most important is necessary to not get caught in other's wants, needs, or *shoulds*. This can only hinder growth."

Sohac sat quietly while listening to the correspondent. He had never realized how passionate this man could be about his work. Nonetheless, this kind of thing could only bring chaos to their organized village. He had calmed down a bit but still needed to stand his ground. He told the correspondent that what he had written could only create confusion and allow for weaknesses that would lead to someone, or all of them, being destroyed. These kinds of things also deterred people from their focus and responsibilities. "It certainly would not be effective for the children to hear anyone talking of the concepts as being really possible," he continued.

Sohac softened his voice a bit, but in a no-nonsense tone said, "Look, I know you want to write about more. But these are not the concepts you should be writing about. You must remember your purpose and duties to this village." The correspondent knew this was the end of the conversation. Feeling defeated, he thanked Sohac for coming by and assured him he understood what he was saying. With that, Sohac left and returned to the manor.

The following morning, the correspondent had an unexpected visitor—the pastor. The pastor wondered what had prompted him to write the article and where his information had come from. He also wanted to know more about actually applying the concepts discussed in the newsletter to daily living. The correspondent shared with the pastor that Sohac had paid him a visit yesterday and told him he needed to forget about the concepts and not write about them anymore. "Actually, I really don't know much more and I don't have answers to your questions, Pastor," replied the correspondent.

The pastor said that he was enthralled with the article and was going to continue looking for more information on the concepts. "I will keep you posted on what I find," he said as he got up to leave. He stopped and turned back on his way out. Sensing a defeated air from the correspondent, he said, "I really think you have uncovered something very good here—listen to your heart."

Later that afternoon, as the correspondent walked back to his office after having lunch at home, he ran into the blacksmith's wife. She spoke excitedly, "Oh, I am so glad to have caught you today. I want to tell you how much I enjoyed your article. I really think you have opened our eyes to something but I still have some questions. My husband even read the article twice!"

The correspondent thanked her for her acknowledgement and felt the need to say, "I appreciate your kind words, but I really have no answers to your questions, and I don't think I will be writing any more like that. Have a good day." At that, he left her and returned to his office. Puzzled, the blacksmith's wife watched the correspondent walk away and decided that she was going to reread the article and talk to her husband and children about the new ideas. She had a feeling that Greyson and Adrie could help her find some answers.

Upon returning to his office, the correspondent sat down and couldn't help but wonder about the concepts in the article. He definitely had stirred something in others. That was evident by his visits today. He wondered how many more people in the village felt as he did. He was frustrated at knowing so little about these new ideas and not being able to answer the questions. He decided he needed to spend some time with Maila. Maybe she could shed some light on all this.

Meanwhile, the article the correspondent wrote was indeed affecting much of the village. The pastor decided to return to the church and research the archives. The blacksmith's wife decided that she wanted to try to bring everyone together to hear their thoughts about the letter and also to start to rally people together.

That morning, the blacksmith had decided he was going to spend some time with his son and daughter and share a secret with them. He had gone out to the back of the shop late the night before after reading the article again and uncovered a huge, old wooden chest. It had been years since he had opened the keepsake. The chest had lots of hand tools, chunks of wood, and small carved figures. There was also a section with a collection of

fishing flies and tools to make them. He remembered back to the time when he and his father would sit and make flies by the fire and go out at the crack of dawn to try them out. He used to love fishing with his father. His father had also been a very accomplished woodworker. Besides figurines and toys, he would create beautiful woodwork for houses, furniture, and more. As he rummaged through the collection, he was taken aback by the memories of such special times and what a sense of loss he now felt. He wasn't doing anything that brought that sense of joy or accomplishment to him, let alone, building those kind of memories with his children. He vowed he would change that, at least with the children.

At breakfast he told Greyson and Adrie that he had a surprise for them, and after they finished eating they were to meet him out at the shop. They rushed through breakfast and ran to the shop. The blacksmith opened the door and saw their beaming faces. "Oh, to have that carefree, peaceful presence!" he thought. The children never seemed to be affected by the monotony of the village. He shook himself out of his reverie and asked the children to follow him. He showed them to the back room and then opened the huge chest. They both gasped with excitement and asked him where it had come from. He told them about their grandfather and the things that he and his father used to do together. "I want to do those things with you both," he replied.

"But when?" replied Greyson, "You have all the blacksmith duties and you are on wall rotation now."

"I have decided I am going to make the time. I am going to cut my hours at the shop and leave every Friday at noon. That way, I can give you lessons in wood carving after I close the shop and we can go fishing on Friday afternoons and Saturday mornings," their father replied.

Both Greyson and Adrie were excited. "Can we go fishing this Friday?" asked Adrie.

"Yes, definitely!" replied her father.

The blacksmith's wife was thrilled at the change in her husband and his new commitment to share with the children. She decided she would try to begin building that same spirit into the village by planning a social event. Her first thought was to go talk with the pastor's wife and ask her to share in the decorating and event planning. She hesitated, not being sure if the pastor's wife would share her reaction to these newfound thoughts. So she decided to cautiously approach her plan without assistance for now. She sat down to work on the details for the event.

Meanwhile, the pastor had gone back to the church office where his heart was heavy. He had several of his parishioners come to him and ask about the meaning of the article. Like the correspondent, he did not have the answers he wished for. Yet there was something pulling at his own heart. Something about these messages sounded so familiar. He decided to take the afternoon to search for answers. He went up to the attic in the old wing of the church. There, amongst the dust and cobwebs, he found files of sermons preached by himself and others before him. Here, among the wonderful history, he came across a series of sermons his own pastor had preached when he was a child. There they were—sermons of a better time— a time of living by your values, taking care of yourself and others, and other messages similar to the correspondent's article. How could there be such similarities through so many years and so much change? This was when it came to him. He must study these wise messages and deliver them in his sermon on Sunday. He set about the task, refreshed, excited, and feeling more purposeful than he had felt in a long time. In fact, he was so excited about the prospect of delivering something heartfelt and true that he went to find Finnian to assist him. He felt Finnian could help him in this endeavor as he was impressed and proud of the job his son was doing with the children's sermons. As he entered the house, he asked his wife if she had seen Finnian. She responded, "No, I haven't. Why are you looking for him?" She was surprised to see the grin on her husband's face and the anxiousness in his mannerism. She asked what he was up to, and he couldn't contain the information he had discovered. He said, "You won't believe what I found in the archives! I found the past sermons that taught the lessons the correspondent wrote about in his latest newsletter."

His wife looked at him in dismay. "I really don't feel that they would be appropriate for a sermon. And, you certainly shouldn't involve our son in that. He already has so many misguidings." Some of the pastor's enthusiasm started to dissipate, but he assured her that he would not do anything he felt was misguiding to either his son or his parishioners. At that point he politely dismissed himself and decided to go work on the sermon alone.

• • •

While so many were intrigued by the messages of the correspondent's newsletter, the sheriff was in a very different frame of mind. "What has happened to my friend, and how could he have gotten so misdirected?" he silently questioned. He remembered the times before, but knew for sure that there was the TruSlayer dragon. After all, he had lost his wife and her family to this awful demon. His deepest thought was that if this creature had not killed his wife, then that would mean she had simply left her family. This would be too terrible to even think, let alone believe. No, there was nothing of truth in the correspondent's article. "It was all lies!!!" he thought vehemently. He tore the newsletter up and threw it away. He stormed out of the house on his way to confront the correspondent. As he rounded the corner, he ran right into the correspondent's wife. She noticed the look on the sheriff's face and had an inkling that it may be due to what her husband had written. It dawned on her the ramifications her husband's thoughts would have on the sheriff. She immediately felt the need to calm him.

She asked, "How are you doing today Sheriff?"

"Not well. Where would I find your husband?" he asked.

"Well, I think I saw him heading off with Maila. Maila mentioned how close she and McKarin are becoming. Maila has been so happy lately. She has been humming and singing the most enchanting songs. In fact, her love of music has given me a great idea to start a music class for our children at school. Wouldn't that be wonderful to brighten their lives with the arts? I believe I will begin working on that first thing tomorrow!" she continued to exude.

A bit taken aback by her commentary, yet sensing her concern, the sheriff calmed himself a bit and politely replied, "I do realize Maila and McKarin have been spending more time together. I have always enjoyed Maila so. She is a bright girl." At this, he decided to simply return to his office and complete his work for the day.

The correspondent's wife sighed with relief as she watched the sheriff head back to his office, but she couldn't help feeling a sense of sadness for him. She realized this was probably raising a lot of questions in his mind. His wife had been a dear friend of hers and she also had to wonder what really happened to her if what her husband had written was really true.

Chapter 6

The Proof

Things seemed to settle down a bit in the village over the next few days. Those who felt a need to act upon their excitement from the concepts in the newsletter did so, but quietly. On Friday, the pastor's wife started upon her normal routine of finding the Sunday sermon to prepare the church and make final arrangements. As she reviewed the sermon, she was shocked that her husband had actually decided to go ahead with a focus on those outlandish thoughts from the newsletter. She quickly sought him out and vehemently warned him that delivering that kind of sermon could create false hopes for the villagers and anger Sohac. He asked her to sit down and allow him to voice his mission and purpose. "I believe in my heart that this information needs to be delivered. I have a responsibility as a spiritual leader in this community to ensure that all messages are available for those who seek guidance. I would not be following my beliefs if I were not to give people the chance to know this information. I ask that you please trust in me and this mission in which I so strongly believe."

She felt very uncomfortable, for she had never disagreed with him on his sermons. She knew this scared her, but didn't know why. She shared with him, "I fear this could make you lose any freedom you have in living your passion."

"But I see the chance to finally, really share that passion with others, which is my purpose," he implored.

She couldn't argue with him at this point. With fear still lingering, she knew she wanted to trust him. "I trust you and understand that you must listen to your heart. It is a good guide," she sighed.

They went back to the church together to prepare for Sunday. He wanted it to look different from their normal subdued atmosphere. He asked what she could do about bringing more color into the church. Reluctantly, she agreed to look into it and went to find more materials.

Sunday morning the pastor was very excited. For the first time in a very long time he felt *led* in what he was about to share. Taking the pulpit, he lovingly looked out across his parishioners. He studied each face and thought about the message he was about to deliver and its impact on each of their lives. He began with such joy. "My loved ones, I am so excited you are here today with me and my family in our house of worship. This week has been a unique time in our community. Our correspondent has really shaken us out of our comfort zones, hasn't he?" the pastor humorously smiled. "But may I share my personal journey this past week," he continued. He told them about his research and his discovery of messages delivered years before. He talked about the need for rebuilding the reserves of community. "Together we can build a fellow-ship stronger, more trusting, and more filled with happi-ness. We must find the way to trusting each other again!" People's reactions ranged from an increased excitement to dismay and discomfort.

The pastor noticed, as the sermon continued, a few of the parishioners departed early. He had hoped people could keep an open mind but understood that fear was still a part of their world. As he concluded the sermon and people began to leave, he noticed a group who lingered, and he went to talk with them. He was anxious to hear people's response. This group was passionately discussing the lessons of the sermon. As he approached, they had many questions for him. He felt a sense of accomplishment and he was prepared to answer most of their questions. He was very excited when the blacksmith's wife mentioned she had already developed the plan for a village event. The blacksmith's wife envisioned an event more lively and grand than those in the past—a festival! She asked if the pastor and his wife would like to help her with the preparations. "I certainly would," answered the pastor, "but my wife is still very hesitant. I would recommend contacting the village school teacher since she has already discussed bringing more music into the church and school." The blacksmith's wife agreed she would contact the village school teacher and welcome her input.

Two weeks later, the pastor included in his sermon some of the remarkable changes that had begun to appear in the village. "I am amazed to report to you my observations of our beloved village. Has anyone else recognized a skip in our step these days? I have been so excited about the positive, healthier attitude of our people. Do you know that there are reports of less illness over the past few weeks than there has been in the past few years? It seems that there is not only more color in our sanctuary but more color in our lives!" he continued. Many were nodding their heads in agreement. In general everyone seemed to be paying more attention to everything around them.

The kids were much more involved with the village activities. Finnian was delivering the children's sermons regularly, and the children were so enjoying his humor and cleverness. Greyson, with his newly learned skills from his father, was busy building props, toys, and carving unique figurines to be given away at the upcoming village festival that his mother was so busily planning. Adrie and Maila were also busy helping with decorations and both were coordinating and giving music lessons.

As the pastor completed his uplifting message and the parishioners were beginning to leave, they heard a commotion coming from the outskirts of town. In horror, they realized that the fields were on fire.

Many cried out, "Oh no, not again!" They all rushed toward the fields and began rallying together to put out the fires. They began a water brigade. Several hours later, the fields were nothing more than a smoking plot of black muck. While they were thrilled with their accomplishment of putting out the fires, they all left exhausted and very saddened. "What happened here today? Is the TruSlayer dragon back again? We know our wall has begun to crumble and show wear, but have we allowed the safety of our village to become this vulnerable?" These were but a few of their weary thoughts as they left that day.

Early the next morning, Sohac called a town meeting and demanded a resurgence of focus and attention to the Wall of Protection to keep the village safe. However, this time things were a bit different. Because of the new sense of community being felt by the villagers and because they had begun to know each other better, they saw each other as true resources. To Sohac's surprise and dismay, the villagers decided to go about correcting things in their own way.

Returning to his manor, Sohac was furious. "I cannot understand how these unappreciative people could go off in their own direction. Especially after all I have done for them!" He began yelling for his clan to come and join him.

Outside, Adrie was enjoying the garden as she often did each day. She was about to knock on the door to give Sohac his daily flower arrangement when she overheard the yelling. Adrie gasped as she heard Sohac talking about how he and his clan had set the fires to the fields. She could scarcely believe her ears. She was shocked and torn but knew she must tell Finnian. She slowly and silently maneuvered her way around the corner hedge and ran to the gate. She headed straight toward the church where Finnian had said he would be. Out of breathe and terribly shaken, she threw herself into Finnian's arms and cried. He held her, amazed at her reaction. "Adrie, come on, what is going on?" he questioned.

"Oh, Finnian, I have just overheard the most horrible thing! It's too terrible to really believe!" she cried.

Finnian sat her down in the nearby pew and grabbed his handkerchief and handed it to her. "Tell me what happened Adrie," Finnian calmly pressed.

"Well, I was up at the manor and went to give Sohac his daily bouquet. As I was about to knock on the door, I heard Sohac yelling at his clansmen. He yelled at them about not setting enough of the fields on fire and that it had been too easy to put out. I can't believe he was behind all this!" Adrie sobbed.

Finnian looked at her in dismay. "Did they see you?" he asked.

"No, at least I don't think so," Adrie answered.

"If this is true Adrie, the village people will lash out at him. I don't know if we should tell them," Finnian whispered.

Adrie let out a big sigh. "I don't know Finnian, I have never kept anything from my parents, especially something so big. But, I also feel bad about overhearing the conversation. Tonight is the Festival. Let's just wait until afterwards so that we don't ruin everyone's evening," Adrie thought out loud.

"All the more reason why it is good that Sohac knows nothing about the Festival," Finnian reflected. They both just sat for a while and talked about what this all might really mean. Neither of them seemed to want to leave. They finally decided they needed to go and dress for the evening's Festival. As they neared the door to the church, Finnian took Adrie's hand. "Listen Adrie, I think we should wait and talk to McKarin, Maila, and Greyson before we do anything more with the information we have," he implored.

"I don't know Finnian. I just don't know what is right at this point," Adrie replied. Adrie gave Finnian a hug and ran out the door toward home.

The community center was beautiful. The decorations so captured the cheerfulness they had hoped to convey. Everything was ready. Games and toys had been made and prepared for the children with brightly colored party favors, sweet cakes, and cider. The musicians were setting up in the corner and testing their instruments. The center of the room had even been cleared so people might dance. Refreshments covered the tables at the side of the room and people were starting to arrive.

In a very short time, the community center was filled with people milling about and mingling. Everyone seemed to be having a good time except the sheriff who sat in the corner by himself.

Even though Adrie had been able to put aside her troubling thoughts about Sohac and enjoy the celebration, the evening was now coming to a close and the nagging feelings came back to her. She knew she had to tell someone. She decided that she would tell her father on the way back to the house.

Chapter 7

Putting Away the Past

The morning after the festival, McKarin called her father to breakfast. After her second attempt, she ascended the old wooden staircase to her father's room. There in the chair looking out the window she saw her father's slumped shoulders. She noticed in his hand the picture of her mother that he always kept next to his bedside.

She saw him wipe a tear from his cheek and her first reaction was to run to comfort him. Yet, her years of being the *strong one* held her back from acting on that soft emotion. She had noticed that her father did not join in the celebration the night before and also understood he was feeling hurt and confused. She knew she had to tell him the whole story, but feared he would not see the truth without something tangible to prove it.

She decided she must find that proof. She silently stepped back into the hall and ran down the stairs. She grabbed a piece of paper and with a shaky hand, wrote a note to her father.

Father,

I love you dearly. I must go and find something. I promise I will return very soon. Trust in me.

Love,
McKarin

She grabbed a chunk of bread, cheese, apples, and water and shoved them in a knapsack. She flew out the door and set her path to the mountaintop with hopes that Arabella would be there.

Her mind was whirling with all the possible ways to prove to her father that her mother did not desert them. She looked up and was amazed that she was already at the foot of the mountain. She had been so deep in thought as she had crossed the fields. She finally started her trek up the winding paths along the mountainside. She knew the way well by now. She was becoming more and more anxious. As she drew closer to the top, she started to worry because she did not hear Arabella's ever-present flute playing.

McKarin called out to Arabella. Nothing. She continued to ascend the mountain. Once she rounded the last bend, there was Arabella looking toward the horizon — almost as if she had been expecting her. She turned and with a knowing smile asked McKarin to come sit next to her and share her thoughts. After hearing McKarin's response, Arabella stated, "I can give you a piece of tangible proof, but the real proof is within you. You are your mother's daughter. Allow your father to see that." McKarin was a bit confused by her words. At that point, Arabella moved her hands to her throat and sighed. She then removed the chain and magnificent stone pendant that she wore. She held it in her hand and looked at it longingly. With tears in her eyes she looked at McKarin and said, "This is the only piece of my sister, Rhianna, that I thought I had left, but now I have you. This belongs to

you because it was your mother's." Amazed by this revelation, McKarin felt the warmth spread through her, and at that moment, she let go of the strong outer shell she hid behind. This answered so many of her remaining questions. As Arabella placed the necklace around her neck, McKarin felt her mother within her and knew what she would say to her father.

Saddened, but anxious to return to her father, McKarin hugged Arabella and kissed her on the cheek. They held each other for a long moment. "Thank you for this precious gift, my aunt," she said. She then turned and headed down the path. She looked back once and waved. She felt a strange pang and realized that Arabella had given up something very precious to her and that she may not see Arabella again. In her anxiousness to return, she put the feeling aside and continued on.

McKarin swiftly traversed the paths down the mountain. She stopped at the base to sit and replenish her energy. She had learned well from Arabella the need to keep herself strong and the need to restore reserves in order to be her best for others. As she continued on her way, she began to realize how different she was feeling. There seemed to be a weight lifted off her shoulders and a sense of peace within her heart. She felt no need to be anything other than her true self, who she was now discovering.

By nightfall she was almost home. She saw the lights of the house, and there was a lantern on the front porch. As she came closer to the house, she saw her father sitting on the front porch. She knew he was anxiously awaiting her return.

As soon as McKarin's father saw her coming, he stood and started toward her. As she came closer, he suddenly stopped. His heart leapt and he raised the lantern. His first thought was that the darkening night was playing tricks on his eyes. But as McKarin came closer he knew it was his daughter, but she looked different. Her hair had fallen down and was free flowing, and then he spotted the necklace around her neck. It took him a moment, but the realization started to unfold. He dropped the lantern and ran to her. Holding her in his arms, he cried and felt the past come rushing back.

The tears came from a sense of relief, joy, and unanswered questions, and for the first time for both of them, a sense of hope. McKarin took her father's hand as they walked back to the house. She said, "Father, I have so much to tell you."

Her father replied, "And I am ready to listen and I know I have so much to learn."

As McKarin put on a pot of tea, she passionately began sharing her journey of discovery and revelations. She revealed, that until this day, she had not fully understood the whole truth. At that point, McKarin explained Arabella's identity as her mother's sister and, with tears in her eyes, explained how she came upon the necklace. She shared the tales of how desperately and fearlessly her mother had fought to return to them. But, she had been defeated by the very wall that the village allowed to be built around them, the same wall that they were led to believe would protect them. She continued to explain that she now understood how false those beliefs really were. The village, and all within, had given in to someone else's beliefs at the cost of their own. Through her tears, she passionately vowed that unless they carried on all that her mother and the others had died for, there would never be any complete peace and harmony. "We owe it to her, to them, to ourselves, and we owe it to our future generations!"

She looked over at her father to see his reaction to all of this. He sat staring at her. She saw the love and acceptance in his eyes. "Oh, how like your mother you really are!"

he exclaimed. "I can't believe I have tried to stifle that all these years because I was bitter, confused, and had lost touch with my own heart and beliefs." They talked on for hours of how they so foolishly allowed the TruSlayer dragon to stay alive in their hearts and minds because of the constant reliance upon the false beliefs and fears. They knew what they had to do. Exhausted from the revelations and the day's discoveries, they begrudgingly said goodnight to one another and climbed the stairs to their rooms for some rest.

• • •

As the sun began to rise, McKarin awoke to a frantic knocking on the door downstairs. She threw on her wrap and quickly descended the stairs. As she opened the door, in flew Adrie and Finnian. They both seemed frantic and upset. Adrie began saying, "I don't think it is supposed to be this way. We need help!"

Finnian exclaimed, "We thought we were doing the right thing and making things better!" McKarin ushered them in and told them to slow down, back up, and explain to her what had upset them so.

Finnian calmed down and explained that he and Adrie had been playing in the back of her father's shop where they had been told not to. They heard her father come in with a few of the other village people, so they crept up to the loft to avoid being noticed. They found themselves witnesses to a small village meeting and couldn't believe their ears. The people of the village were planning to besiege Sohac's manor and fight until they banished Sohac and his clan from the village. "People will get hurt and may even die if this happens!" said Adrie. "I'm so sorry I told my father that I had overheard Sohac talking about setting the fires in the field."

"McKarin, we thought maybe your father could stop this," they stated.

McKarin sat down for a minute to think through all she had heard. She then told them about her discoveries from yesterday and that her father was in a different place now as well. Not knowing for sure how her father would react to all this, yet knowing in her heart the villagers' plan was not abiding by the lessons Arabella had taught them, McKarin suggested that they contact Maila and Greyson and all work through this together.

McKarin went to get dressed and asked Adrie and Finnian to go get Greyson and Maila. They would meet at the old willow tree just outside the gates.

An hour later, they were all sitting underneath the willow tree. Adrie and Finnian had filled everyone in on what they had heard in the shop and what Adrie had heard the day she went to the manor. "So, what should we do?" asked Finnian.

"We need to stop them," replied Maila.

"Oh, I don't know," chimed Greyson. "Sohac has misled us all these years and now has deliberately tried to sabotage the village."

Adrie immediately jumped in and reminded them of the compassionate and caring person she had learned Sohac could be. "His kindnesses toward me, and the others on occasion, cannot be dismissed," she added.

At this point McKarin reminded everyone that the lessons learned from Arabella taught them to put aside judgments and work toward harmony and forgiveness and that it was now up to them to help both sides see clearly. They must see each and every person in the village with compassion and understanding and communicate clearly. "We must find a way to guide both sides through this," she continued, "we must create a united front and go speak peacefully with our village."

Before they had a chance to stand up to leave, Maila's younger brother came running out to the tree and announced that McKarin's father was going to lead an attack on Sohac's manor.

They all looked at each other and knew in their hearts what each needed to do. Adrie and Finnian headed to Sohac's manor to warn him. Greyson and Maila went to talk with the people, and McKarin quickly rushed to find her father to try to reason with him and remind him what her mother really had been trying to do. Before they parted, they hugged each other and wished each other well. They hoped they would be the united front that would end the discord that had grown within their little part of the world.

Adrie and Finnian found Sohac in his garden. They explained the day's events and what the village people were planning. His first reaction was to call together his clan to fight against the uprising until Adrie rested her hand on his arm. With her huge blue eyes she pleaded with him to see the perspective of the villagers and to not fight. She implored, "Please hear them out, and see the villagers for the wonderful people they really are, and be honest with them."

"There need not be any fighting. The uprising is due to misunderstandings and false beliefs," Finnian stressed.

Sohac agreed to talk with the villagers but also was firm in that he would have his clan ready and prepared if an attack was made. "We must protect ourselves," he claimed.

Adrie and Finnian agreed to this and Adrie said, "We will meet you at the manor gates in one hour."

Back at the village McKarin pleaded with her father to talk in private for just a few moments. Her father finally agreed. Greyson and Maila took that opportunity to move to the front of the group that had assembled. They spoke passionately from their hearts of the lessons they had been learning and living during the past eight months. They asked the people in the group what changes had occurred in their lives and in the village as a result of the things that the children had been doing and others following their lead. Many acknowledged that things had been positively different and they liked the new ways. Greyson and Maila soon realized that it was the acknowledgment of these lessons that reminded the villagers of what they had lost. They all wanted to regain what was lost. Maila and Greyson looked at each other and understood what they were saying but didn't know how to convince them that the approach they were taking was not in accord with the beliefs they so wanted to regain. They stepped aside feeling defeated and helpless. McKarin joined them, and the strain of trying to convince her father showed on her face. The passion of the crowd ignited and festered. The three quickly ran out to find Adrie and Finnian. They found them at the base of the drive to Sohac's manor. They all knew now that words were not enough to dissipate the fire that had been fueled. They looked up toward the manor and saw Sohac and his clan emerge. They turned around to find the villagers moving toward the manor with a fierceness that was frightening.

McKarin felt the warmth of her necklace on her chest. She held it and silently reached out to her mother and all those from the past who fought to keep alive the beliefs that nurtured and kept their people whole. She started to sing the song Arabella had taught them. One by one the children joined hands, and the five of them started up the hill toward the manor and sang in unison. When they reached the gates, Adrie stepped forward toward the gate and held out her hand to Sohac. By this point, the villagers had ascended the hill and McKarin turned and stepped toward the crowd. She held out her hand to her father. Then, as if by magic, Arabella came from behind the stone column of the gate. She was playing her flute and everyone stopped to listen. As she came closer to the children, sighs and gasps of disbelief were heard throughout the crowd as many of them recognized her as the young woman who so many years ago had left with her sister, Rhianna. The villagers had known that Arabella and others had gone in search of the truth. Since they had never returned, it was believed the TruSlayer dragon had killed the women and the others. With her now standing before them, memories of better days, filled with happiness and abundance, came flooding back. Then, the questions started to surface. Where had she been? Was there really a TruSlayer dragon? Why was she reappearing now?

Arabella stepped forward and introduced herself. She explained, "I have returned to help you see clearly the secrets that lie within each of you. By choosing to believe in the false beliefs and fears, you allowed yourselves to be misguided. Yet, remember, the people who planted those fears and doubts did so because they truly believed them, not necessarily for malicious reasons. Sohac simply

planted seeds of doubt and false beliefs and all of you nurtured them, allowing those doubts to grow and survive,
and therefore, losing your Tru•Self. The children have
been trying to help you see that you can change those false
beliefs. It is now up to all of you to choose what kind of
values and beliefs you want to encompass in your lives.
These children have proven to me that they have given up
the false beliefs and have found their Tru•Self. This, in turn,
has killed the TruSlayer dragon, which always only existed
in the minds of its creators. They are the ones who have
moved toward their optimal beings," Arabella concluded.

Arabella walked over to the children and hugged
each one. She then handed the flute to Adrie and kissed
her on the cheek. "Adrie, you are a true spirit and find listening to your heart comes so easily. I entrust to you the
flute. You are the one who knows how to make it sing so
sweetly." She walked over to Finnian, "Finnian, you are
the constant reminder of passion. Your actions come from
the heart and you see every moment with a new light and
message. I entrust to you these glass stones." She
explained, "Each one of these stones represents one of the
beliefs recaptured—hold them dearly and keep them for
those who need reminding." She turned to Maila and said,

"Maila, you are so responsible. You have a gift of communicating messages so appropriately for all to understand. I entrust to you the mission of this land. Keep it visible and allow it to rightfully evolve with the help of others." She turned to Greyson, "Greyson you are the one who considers all and helps to hold on to the traditions that make us who we are. I entrust to you the crest of this land. Display it proudly and protect it." She then turned to McKarin and hugged her deep and long. "I have already given you your gifts. It is now up to you to carry on your mother's legacy. Listen to your heart. Children, I bid you farewell but know I will always be a part of you."

As quickly as she came, she was gone. The children all looked at each other and knew they would never see her again. They looked at their gifts. Adrie started to play the flute, Finnian and Maila unrolled the mission for all to see, and Greyson and McKarin walked to the manor gate and asked Sohac if they could raise the crest. Sohac stammered for a moment, but knew that the right thing to do was to allow them to reclaim this legacy. They slowly unfurled the soft and delicate fabric. As they raised it, the crest emerged. It was beautifully colored and had a symbol that represented greatness coming together. But it was the words within the symbol that made them finally realize the truth in Arabella's words. The crest read *The Land of Optimalia.* The realization seemed to slowly spread through the crowd. This was the crest from their past that they had so easily forgotten. They had allowed themselves to be misguided and lose their way of life. Between the music of the flute and the laughing and joyous shouts from the children, a new light came over the village and one by one the people felt the false beliefs and fears begin to melt away.

Chapter 8

New Beginnings

Now was the moment of truth for Sohac. He had to come to terms with his warring feelings and the turmoil inside himself. Should he warn these people that they should not so easily accept all that was unfolding before them or did he feel deep in his heart the need to also let go of the false beliefs and fears that kept *him* so locked within himself? After watching the children so joyously celebrate, he couldn't help but believe that they were the essence of truth and inherently knew how to live by their heart's guide. He also knew it wasn't that easy to let go of the warning in his mind. This determined his course of action. He must leave and allow these people to rekindle what they

had lost. His quest would be to find the pieces he needed to clarify his own beliefs.

Sohac opened the gates and stepped forward. McKarin's father also stepped forward and said, "There must be a peaceful way to cross this bridge."

Sohac responded, "Although I agree with you, I cannot as easily put away the images and false beliefs of my past as all of you can. You all have memories that are closer to you. I don't know how far I can go at this point. I do believe I need to leave to seek these pieces of my past." Sohac then turned to acknowledge the children. Knowing this would be the hardest part for him, he took a deep breath and said, "This parting is harder than you know. I recognize what you have tried to do to bring us all together and bring back the way of life that should be. I want you to know I respect this greatly. Out of this respect, I think it is time for me to move on even though it is very difficult to leave this place."

Adrie ran to him and they hugged. Finnian reached in his bag of stones and handed him the stone that had the word *Optimal* etched on it. He handed Sohac the stone and said, "May you always remember us." Sohac took the stone and held it. A tear came to his eye.

He thanked Finnian with a heartfelt handshake and turned to Adrie and said, "I give to you my gardens and hope that you will continue to care for them as you have." Sohac then turned to the people and announced, "I give back to you, *The Land of Optimalia*, and this manor. May it be the place your community gathers and I ask from you in return that the gates always remain open to myself or others who cross this way and ask to enter your world."

At that point Sohac turned to his clan and said, "Those of you who know you cannot stay and let go of your false beliefs may go with me. Those of you who feel that this is the place for you, I acknowledge your desire to follow your heart and wish you well. You must make the best choice for yourselves." With that said, he turned with a heavy heart to go and seek his own discoveries. As he rode away, the clouds parted and a beautiful ray of sun shone on the village. Its warmth and light was a statement that a new village was emerging and that *The Land of Optimalia* had been rediscovered.

— The End —

Afterword

It has been a long journey to this point! Many pathways were traveled, many detours endured, and many glorious sights observed along the trail. We met several years ago via a training venture. It took very little time to respect and honor one another. It was amazing and truly a blessing to uncover that we shared a passion for the same personal growth concepts. We put our experiences and knowledge together to build a program that would help individuals discover and develop the life skills needed to live an optimal life. In reading *The Secrets That Lie Within*, our hope for you is that you experienced a unique journey in finding your Tru•Self™ and moving toward optimal being. In a society where we can get so "turned around" and can experience such chaos, we wish you a life of *"rising to the top of the mountain"* and discovering what is needed to be successful and happy.

Through the journey of writing this fable, we discovered how difficult it is to combine the tasks of building awareness, without overwhelming, and yet describing the "how" of finding your Tru•Self™. Hence, we wrote *The Secrets That Lie Within* to build the foundation for your journey to an optimal life. There are three sequels to follow *The Secrets That Lie Within* that will portray the pathways to travel in finding your Tru•Self™ and moving toward your optimal being. Please visit us at our website often, www.tru-skills.com, to look for updates on the progress and publication dates for the continuance of this series.

The concepts from this story and the sequels to follow all come from our program, *Tru•Skills®: An Individual Development Process*. This unique development program takes the participant through a personally guided journey of discovery and enlightenment. The journey entails experiencing the pathways of:

Connections
❧
Life Mapping
❧
Living "In-Choice"
❧
Rich Reserves
❧
Life Pacing
❧
Calming Chaos
❧
The Draw Theory
❧
Extreme Care
❧
Optimal Being

We hope you will join us in an upcoming session of *Tru•Skills®: An Individual Development Process.*

We welcome you to visit our website at www.tru-skills.com for further information regarding Tru•Skills®, program registration, and other products, services, and updates.

May you discover your Tru•Self™ and live the optimal life you were destined to live!

Kerry   *Vicky*

Kerry Hearns-Smith and Vicky Arledge

About the Authors

Kerry Hearns-Smith is President and Owner of Innovative Development Techniques, a firm dedicated to helping individuals and organizations discover new horizons through developing and unleashing human potential. She is an energetic, motivational and insightful, professional coach, training and development facilitator/consultant, national speaker and author. Her passion is to help others discover and move closer to their true potential. Kerry's educational background is in Psychology with an emphasis in Industrial/Organizational Psychology and Educational Leadership. She is a member of the American Society of Training and Development, International Coaching Federation, Coach University, National Association of Female Executives and Publishers Marketing Association. Kerry makes her home in the beautiful resort town of Whitehall, Michigan with her husband Mike, their two children, Keaton and Kiera, and their cat Nike.

Vicky Arledge is President and Owner of Vantage Alliance, a firm dedicated to encouraging and enlightening personal and professional growth. In her more than 20 years as a training and development facilitator/consultant, motivational speaker and author, Vicky brings to her audiences a unique combination of creativity, energy, humor, motivation and connectedness. It is her goal to share the lessons of her life experiences with individuals and businesses to assist them in growing toward their potential. Vicky's educational background is in Mathematics Education and she is a member of the American Society of Training and Development, Publishers Marketing Association and International Networking. She has two adult sons, Terry and Tommy, and makes her home in San Antonio, Texas.

In their passion for personal and professional growth and their quest for balance, Kerry and Vicky formed Tru•Skills, LLC and co-authored Tru·Skills®: An Individual Development Process as a culmination of their shared vision of encouraging and supporting individuals in the discovery of their Tru·Self™ and optimal being. They have had the opportunity, through Tru·Skills® and other programs, to assist thousands on their journey in finding their Tru·Self™ and reaching their optimal being-from individuals and small businesses to Fortune 500 companies such as AT&T, Chase Manhattan, ESI International, Fidelity, Prudential, Marriott and Steelcase. The lessons found in Tru·Skills® are the basis for their book *The Secrets That Lie Within* and the three sequels to follow.